The Story of Easter

Christopher Doyle and John Haysom

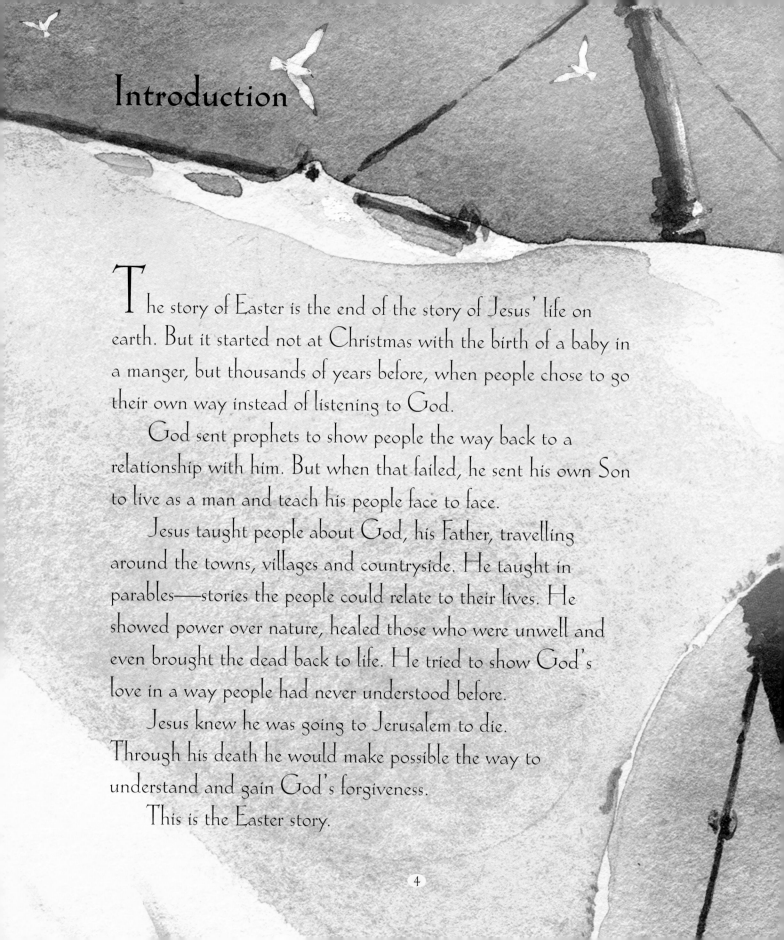

Introduction

The story of Easter is the end of the story of Jesus' life on earth. But it started not at Christmas with the birth of a baby in a manger, but thousands of years before, when people chose to go their own way instead of listening to God.

God sent prophets to show people the way back to a relationship with him. But when that failed, he sent his own Son to live as a man and teach his people face to face.

Jesus taught people about God, his Father, travelling around the towns, villages and countryside. He taught in parables—stories the people could relate to their lives. He showed power over nature, healed those who were unwell and even brought the dead back to life. He tried to show God's love in a way people had never understood before.

Jesus knew he was going to Jerusalem to die. Through his death he would make possible the way to understand and gain God's forgiveness.

This is the Easter story.

'Can you hear the noise? He must be close by now!'

The crowds had waited outside Jerusalem for hours. A man nearby had cut branches from the palm trees. The children waved them in the air, swatting flies and wafting a cooling breeze over their faces. Now at last it seemed their waiting had been worth it.

The cheering grew louder and children craned their necks to see. In the distance, dust rose under trampling feet. Shawls and cloaks were thrown in the air and then laid on the road.

Suddenly they could see their king!

'Look! Jesus is here!' They cheered and shouted along with everyone else.

Sure enough, there was Jesus riding on the back of a donkey. It was not the way people imagined their king would arrive but they didn't care. Young and old, rich and poor, priests and Pharisees had all turned out to see Jesus. The crowd

thronged around him.

Some people inside the gates of the city hadn't heard about what was happening.

'What's all the noise? Who is causing such a stir?' they asked.

'It's Jesus, the prophet from Nazareth in Galilee,' they shouted back and they surged on through the streets following Jesus towards the temple.

In a few days' time it would be Passover.
Many people had come to the temple as
they were taught in the Law of Moses. They
needed special temple coins, birds and
animals to offer as sacrifices. Traders had set
up their stalls and voices echoed through
the courtyard and entrance halls.
Money-changers counted their coins
and clerks scribbled down the accounts
for their masters. Amongst this activity
strode the figure of Jesus.

Suddenly there was an almighty
crash! Coins, pens and inkpots
scattered in all directions. Tables were
overturned and cages holding pigeons split
open as they hit the stone floor. All was chaos as
birds and animals flew and scampered about.

'The Scriptures say this should be a house
of prayer to God,' roared Jesus. 'You have
made it a hiding place for thieves!'

The traders were
overcharging and cheating
people of their hard-earned money.
Some of them cast angry
glances at Jesus as he chased them from
the temple.

The children squealed with delight to
see the animals free. But then others came
to Jesus. Those who were unwell struggled
through the crowds. Jesus welcomed all of
them and healed their illnesses, making blind
people see and lame people walk again.

But watching from the shadows were the
chief priests and teachers of the Law. They
were angry at what they saw Jesus doing.
'We must do something about this
man,' they muttered to each other,
'before he causes more trouble...'

During the days that followed, Jesus taught his disciples and the crowds that flocked to see him. But his new ideas annoyed the temple leaders. Before Passover, they met at the house of Caiaphas, the High Priest, to work out a way to stop Jesus teaching. They discussed how they could arrest Jesus and put him to death. They knew they must take care how they handled it so as not to cause a riot. But all agreed they should look for the right time and a way to carry out their plans.

Meanwhile, in Bethany, Jesus and his disciples were enjoying a meal at Simon's house. As they ate, a woman came in carrying a jar carved from alabaster. All eyes watched her and everyone wondered what was about to happen. The woman opened the jar and very gently poured the contents over Jesus' head. As it trickled down his hair, the scent of perfumed oil filled the room.

Suddenly the spell was broken and the disciples were all talking at once.

'What a waste of expensive ointment!' said one. 'We could have sold that oil and given the money to the poor!'

'Don't be angry with her,' said Jesus. 'This woman has done a beautiful thing. You will always have the poor here to look after, but soon I shall be gone. She has

prepared my body ready for burial.'

One of the disciples, Judas Iscariot, decided then and there to help the Jewish authorities capture Jesus. He went to see the chief priests.

'I can give you Jesus,' he said. 'How much will you pay me to do it?'

They counted out thirty silver coins and handed them to Judas. From then on he looked for an opportunity to betray Jesus.

11

The next evening, Jesus and the disciples were due to eat a special meal, remembering the time the Israelites escaped the death of the eldest child of each family and were led out of Egypt.

A man in the city showed the disciples a room where they could get everything ready and they busied themselves with the preparations. But when evening arrived and everyone was there, Jesus seemed quiet and thoughtful. He knew God had given him the power to do all the things he had

accomplished and that very soon
he would be going back to
God. He also knew the
thoughts in Judas' head.

Before the meal, Jesus stood
up and took off his outer coat.
Pouring water into a basin, he
started to wash the feet of each of
his disciples in turn and dried them off
with a towel. When it came to his turn,
Peter reacted as dramatically as he often did.

'Lord, I shan't ever let you wash my feet!'

'You don't understand what I am doing now, but in time you will,'
replied Jesus. 'And if I don't wash your feet you can't call yourself a friend
of mine.'

'In that case wash them and my hands and head, too!' cried Peter.

'I don't have to do that because you're already clean. But not all of you
here are clean,' Jesus said. That puzzled some of the disciples, but the words
burned into Judas' conscience. He felt he had to get away soon.

Jesus sat back down at the table and explained that as he had washed
their feet like a servant would, they should care for others. It was a way to
help prepare them for the work they would have to do when he had left
them.

Now the food was all laid out on the table. Jesus gave thanks for the meal, handed round some wine and the meal began.

Later, in a quiet moment, Jesus took some of the bread in his hands. He blessed it and then broke it up.

'This is my body,' he said. 'Whenever you eat this, remember me.'

He took a cup of the wine, again blessed it and then held it out to them. He explained it was his blood, sealing the promise God made to forgive the sins of those who love him.

Each of the disciples ate and drank. Then Jesus said something that upset and confused them.

'One of you here will betray me.'

They all whispered amongst themselves, wondering whom Jesus meant. Through the chatter, Jesus turned and told Judas to get on with what he was going to do.

As Judas was in charge of the purse, the others thought he was going to buy more food or give some money to the poor. They didn't really pay much attention as he went out.

But as Judas left the room, he cast a guilty glance over his shoulder...

Afterwards, Jesus and the disciples set off through the night to the Mount of Olives. When they arrived, Jesus turned to the disciples.

'Do you realise that all of you will desert me later tonight?' he asked. Everyone protested and said they wouldn't. Peter declared he would never leave Jesus. He seemed very sure of himself.

'You say that now, but before the cockerel crows twice in the morning you will have denied three times that you know me.'

They came to the garden called Gethsemane. Jesus took Peter, James and John apart from the rest. He admitted to his three friends how scared he was. He knew that all of this was God's plan, but it was still difficult to bear.

'Keep watch here,' said Jesus, and he went off a little way by himself.

In the moonlight Jesus prayed desperately. 'Father, I know you can change what is about to happen, but I am willing to die for you if that's what is needed.'

Jesus went back to see his friends, but now they had fallen asleep. Why couldn't they stay awake for just a while? Jesus prayed again and then a third time, but whenever he returned, the disciples couldn't keep their eyes open.

'Are you still asleep? Come on, the time has arrived. Look, here comes my betrayer.'

Over the hill came a band of soldiers carrying spears and swords. Jesus stood and waited. Out of the shadows into the torchlight stepped Judas. He came forward, gave Jesus the kiss of friendship, then slunk away. This was the sign the troops had been waiting for. Now they surged forward to arrest Jesus. He didn't resist—but the disciples all ran away.

The soldiers wasted no time in marching Jesus to the High Priest's house.

Although all the disciples had run away, Peter returned and followed the soldiers, keeping out of sight. Now he found himself in the courtyard of that same house. He was grateful for the fire there and he warmed his hands as he sat alongside some of the onlookers.

Just as he was settling down, a servant girl came out of the house. She looked straight at Peter and exclaimed that she had seen him with Jesus.

'Who? Him? I don't know him,' Peter declared, shuffling his feet. After a little while a man peered at Peter.

'You are one of the group that went round with him.'

'No, I am not,' Peter protested. He was starting to feel uncomfortable but he still sat there, the fire keeping

away the night chill. About an hour later,
another man finally spoke up.

'You know, I'm certain this man was with
Jesus. You can tell by his accent he comes from
Galilee.'

'I don't know what you're talking
about…' Peter was outraged but, even as he
spoke, in the distance came the sound of a
cockerel crowing in the early morning. Jesus
turned, looked out of the open doors and stared
straight into Peter's eyes. At that moment Peter
remembered what Jesus had said to him earlier in
the night. Peter was devastated. He turned and fled
from the courtyard and broke down in tears.

Meanwhile, as morning grew light, the chief priests and
scribes gathered and led Jesus off to question him at their council
meeting.

The council tried to trick Jesus into saying something they could lay as a charge against him. They twisted his words and dragged him away to the Roman Governor.

Pilate questioned Jesus but could find nothing wrong with his answers. When he discovered Jesus was from Galilee he tried to pass the problem on to King Herod, who was in Jerusalem at the time.

Herod had wanted to see Jesus perform a miracle but he would do nothing, not even answer the questions Herod put to him. The members of the council accused Jesus of all sorts of crimes he had not committed. Finally Herod became bored and sent him back to Pilate.

Now the crowd outside had been roused by the chief priests. They were calling to have a murderer released and Jesus crucified. Pilate ordered that Jesus be whipped.

The soldiers dressed him in a purple robe and one plaited thorn twigs into a crown and pushed it on to his head. They taunted Jesus, slapping and hitting him. Then Pilate took Jesus out to the crowd.

'Look,' said Pilate, 'I don't think this man has done any wrong.'

But the crowd were angry. They told Pilate that if he let Jesus go free then he was not a friend of Caesar. This really worried Pilate. He sat in front of the crowd on the seat of judgment.

'Here is your king!' he said. Seemingly with one voice, the crowd roared back that Jesus should be crucified.

'Shall I crucify your king?' asked Pilate. But he didn't expect an answer. He ordered that Jesus be handed over to the chief priests.

21

In the street Jesus staggered under the weight of the cross he was made to carry to a place called 'The Skull' outside the city.

The watching crowd winced each time the hammer struck home as Jesus' hands and feet were nailed on to the wood. Then he was lifted up and hung next to two other prisoners crucified that day. The three crosses stood out starkly against the sky on the top of the hill.

Pilate had written a notice which read, 'Jesus of Nazareth, King of the Jews'. The rulers of the temple called out to Jesus asking why he didn't save himself as he had saved others. And as the shadows lengthened, the soldiers threw dice and gambled to see which one would have Jesus' robe.

Not far away, the women who had followed Jesus out of the city stood watching everything. Jesus' mother was there too. She had

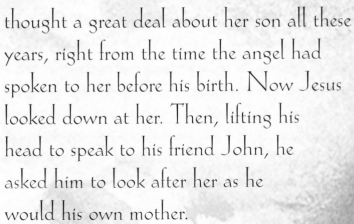

thought a great deal about her son all these years, right from the time the angel had spoken to her before his birth. Now Jesus looked down at her. Then, lifting his head to speak to his friend John, he asked him to look after her as he would his own mother.

Then Jesus cried out, 'It is finished!'

It was over. The crowd began drifting home, feeling very sorry to see Jesus dead.

Later, before it grew dark, Joseph of Arimathea took Jesus' body down from the cross. Wrapping it in a linen cloth he took it to a tomb he had prepared for his own burial. Last thing that day, they rolled a large stone across the entrance to seal the tomb.

23

Very early in the morning, on the day after the Jewish Sabbath, Mary Magdalene crept out of the house. She carried spices and ointments to put on Jesus' body as there had been no time to prepare him properly for burial. In the dawn light things looked different; all was quiet.

When Mary arrived at the garden, she stopped and gasped. The stone had been rolled away and the tomb was empty except for the linen cloth.

Mary stood outside and wept.

She was startled by two angels who were asking why she was crying. She sobbed that she didn't know where Jesus had been taken. Then Mary sensed someone standing behind her. She turned and through her tears saw a figure who spoke to her.

'Why are you crying? Who are you looking for?'

In her confusion and distress Mary thought it was the gardener.

'If you have moved him, tell me where you have put him,' she pleaded. The man spoke again but said only one word.

'Mary!'

Instantly Mary recognised
Jesus and fell down on her knees.

'Teacher,' she cried, tears of joy
now running down her cheeks.

Jesus told Mary to go back and tell
the others what she had seen and that he
would visit them again before he went back
to his Father. Mary ran faster than she ever
had before and poured out the whole story
to the disciples.

The disciples marvelled at Mary's story. Later that evening most of them were together in the upper room of the house. They had the doors locked, scared the Jewish authorities might come after them too. Suddenly, without any warning, Jesus was standing with them in the room.

'May peace be with you,' he said. He showed them the wounds the nails had made in his hands and feet and where the Roman soldier had stuck a spear in his side. The disciples were overjoyed to see him again and talked

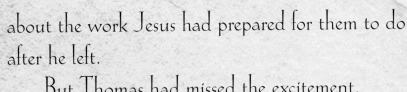

about the work Jesus had prepared for them to do after he left.

But Thomas had missed the excitement.

'It can't be true,' he said when the others told him of Jesus' appearance. 'I won't believe you until I see him myself.'

About a week later, as before, the doors were locked but this time all the disciples were together. Again Jesus came in and stood there with them.

'So, Thomas, you doubt your friends. Here, put your fingers in the marks on my hand. Touch this scar on my side.'

'I don't need to; I can see it is you, my Lord and my God.'

Jesus looked at Thomas.

'Do you believe because you see me? Plenty of others will believe without seeing me and they will be blessed because of it.'

Then Jesus left them again.

Days passed and the disciples went back to their village by the lake in Galilee. One evening Peter was sitting with half a dozen of the others. 'I'd like to go out fishing. Any of you want to come?'

They set off in the boat and worked hard all night, casting the nets but hauling them back in empty. They were on the point of packing everything up when a figure called from the shore.

'Try casting your net on the other side of the boat.'

The disciples were worn out but, expecting nothing, cast the net once more. When they came to haul it in this time, they couldn't believe it; the net was crammed with fish! John shielded his eyes against the sun.

'Hey, Peter!' he cried. 'Look, it's Jesus!'

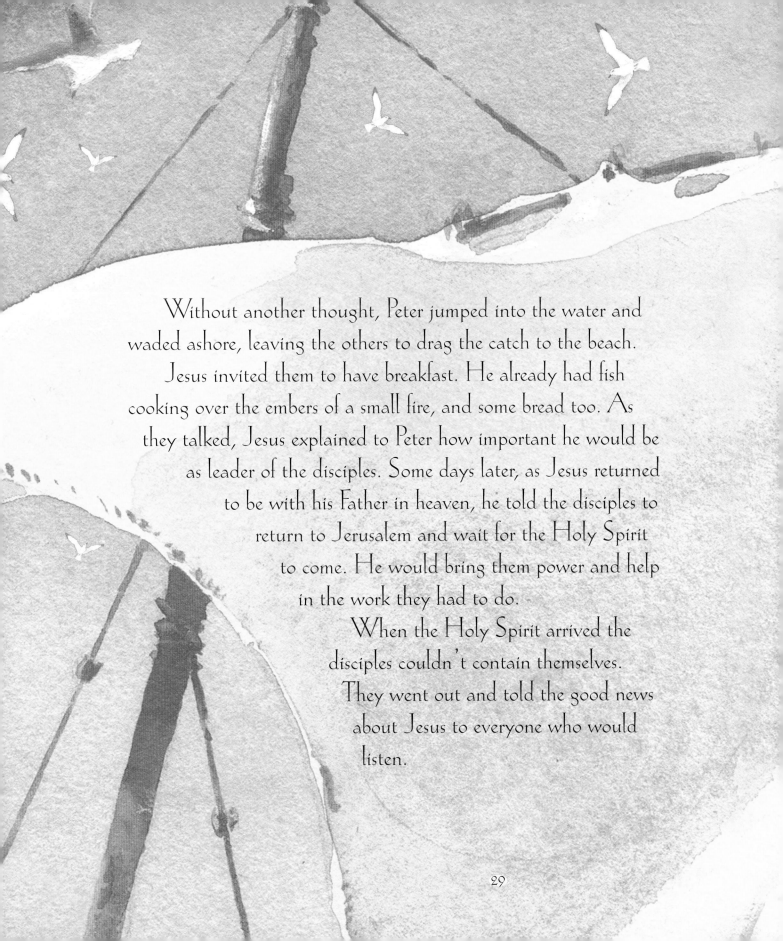

Without another thought, Peter jumped into the water and
waded ashore, leaving the others to drag the catch to the beach.
Jesus invited them to have breakfast. He already had fish
cooking over the embers of a small fire, and some bread too. As
they talked, Jesus explained to Peter how important he would be
as leader of the disciples. Some days later, as Jesus returned
to be with his Father in heaven, he told the disciples to
return to Jerusalem and wait for the Holy Spirit
to come. He would bring them power and help
in the work they had to do.

When the Holy Spirit arrived the
disciples couldn't contain themselves.
They went out and told the good news
about Jesus to everyone who would
listen.